CW00554380

# THE OFFICIAL
# BRISTOL ROVERS
# QUIZ BOOK

# THE OFFICIAL BRISTOL ROVERS QUIZ BOOK

Compiled by Chris Cowlin
and Kevin Snelgrove

Foreword by Ian Holloway and Stuart Taylor

APEX PUBLISHING LTD

Hardback first published in 2008, updated and reprinted in 2009 by

Apex Publishing Ltd

PO Box 7086, Clacton on Sea, Essex, CO15 5WN, England

www.apexpublishing.co.uk

Copyright © 2008 by Chris Cowlin and Kevin Snelgrove
The authors have asserted their moral rights

**British Library Cataloguing-in-Publication Data**
**A catalogue record for this book**
**is available from the British Library**

ISBN HARDBACK:        1-906358-51-6        978-1-906358-51-8

All rights reserved. This book is sold subject to the condition, that no part of this book is to be reproduced, in any shape or form. Or by way of trade, stored in a retrieval system or transmitted in any form or by any means, electronic, mechanical, photocopying, recording, be lent, re-sold, hired out or otherwise circulated in any form of binding or cover other than that in which it is published and without a similar condition, including this condition being imposed on the subsequent purchaser, without prior permission of the copyright holder.

Typeset in 10.5pt Chianti Bdlt Win95BT

Cover Design:  Siobhan Smith

Printed in Great Britain by the MPG Books Group,
Bodmin and King's Lynn

**Author's Note:**
Please can you contact me: **ChrisCowlin@btconnect.com** if you find any mistakes/errors in this book as I would like to put them right on any future reprints of this book. I would also like to hear from Bristol Rovers fans who have enjoyed the test! For more information on me and my books please look at: **www.ChrisCowlin.com**

This book is an official product of Bristol Rovers Football Club.

**We would like to dedicate this book to:**

*All the players and staff who have worked for the club during their history.*

# FOREWORD

What a pleasure and honour to be asked to write the foreword to Chris and Kevin's book.

Being a life long Gashead I like to think I know a thing or two about Bristol Rovers, but then I read this book and realised just how little I did know!

It's an absolute must for us Rovers fans and gave me hours of fun and provoked some wonderful memories, what magic! Test your knowledge and maybe even learn a few more things about the Gas along the way!

I am sure you will enjoy this book as much as I did!

*Yours in football*
*Ian Holloway*

# FOREWORD

*My 15 years as a player with Bristol Rovers took me from 1965 through to 1980. My first eighteen months was as a part-time professional as I was still an apprentice plumber, then aged 20 I signed as a full-time professional.*

*At the time of signing Mr Bert Tann was the manager and was shortly followed by Mr Fred Ford.*

*Larry Lloyd and Ray Grayson were just two of the many up and coming good, young players. There were also some legends at Bristol Rovers, who were coming to the end of their careers, namely Alfie Biggs, Ray Mabbutt and Doug Hillard, to name but a few.*

*During my early years at the club my greatest influence came from Bobby Campbell and Bill Dodgin, we were a very young side but worked hard at our game.*

*At the ripe old age of 33, I was disappointed to have to leave Bristol Rovers. I spent many happy years playing with some very good players which were also friends. I was very fortunate to have avoided any minor injuries through my career.*

*I am very honoured to have been asked to write the foreword to Chris's and Kevin's book, they have put a lot of hard work into it to put all the questions and answers together. It recalled some wonderful memories for me and I am sure all Pirates from the past to the present day will have fun with this book. A great test for all fans and fun for all the family. Enjoy!*

*Best wishes*
*Stuart Taylor*

# INTRODUCTION

*I would first of all like to thank Ian Holloway and Stuart Taylor for writing the foreword to this book. Ian has both played and managed the club so he has seen a lot happen, he is also very well respected by Rovers fans. Stuart is a true legend for Rovers and holds the record for appearing the most times in a Rovers shirt. I am very grateful for their help on this project.*

*I would also like to thank all the past legends of Bristol Rovers Football Club and many current employees of the club for their comments and reviews on this book (these can be found at the back of the book).*

*I would also like to thank Steve Burns for his help and advice during the books compilation.*

*I hope you enjoy this book. Hopefully it should bring back some wonderful memories!*

*It was great working with Kevin Snelgrove again, who is very well organised, between us I hope we have given you a selection of easy, medium and hard questions.*

*In closing, I would like to thank all my friends and family for encouraging me to complete this book.*

*Best wishes*
*Chris Cowlin*

*Visit Chris Cowlin's website:*

*www.ChrisCowlin.com*


*Visit Kevin Snelgrove's website:*

*www.KevinSnelgrove.co.uk*

# HISTORY OF THE CLUB

1. In which year was the club founded – 1883, 1885 or 1887?

2. By what name was Bristol Rovers first called?

3. In which year was the club re-named to Bristol Rovers – 1896, 1898 or 1900?

4. In which year did Rovers turn professional – 1899, 1901 or 1903?

5. Bristol Rovers has two nicknames, can you name them both?

6. Which team are Bristol Rovers biggest rivals?

7. In 1972 Rovers won the Watney Cup, which team did they beat in the final?

8. Rovers first played at Eastville Stadium until they moved in August 1996, what is the name of their new stadium?

9. In May 2008 there were plans for the Memorial Stadium to be demolished, where were Bristol Rovers to play their home games?

10. On 16 February 2008 Bristol Rovers reached the quarter finals of the FA Cup for the first time since 1958. Who were their opponents in the quarter finals in 1958 when they lost 3-1?

# WHO AM I? – 1

11.    I play in goal and signed from Bristol City in July 2006.

12.    I played 467 League games for Rovers and spent over 50 years at the club as player, coach and groundsman.

13.    I am a Welsh defender who signed on a free transfer in July 2007 from Cardiff. I scored my first Rovers goal against Oldham in a 1-0 win during August 2007.

14.    I am a Latvian international and was the most capped player whilst at Bristol Rovers.

15.    I played for Rovers in the late 1970s and early 1980s. My father played for Rovers in the 1950s and 1960s. I won 16 England caps during my career.

16.    I have made the most League appearances for Rovers with 546 appearances scoring 28 goals in my Bristol Rovers career.

17.    I cost Rovers £200,000 from Rochdale in 2006, I was born in Liverpool and play in midfield.

18.    I played for Rovers during 1983/1984 and am the only Rovers player who has won a world cup winners' medal.

19.    I signed from Bournemouth in August 2008, I was a trainee at Arsenal and I am a centre forward.

20.    I had two spells as manager during the 1980s. I managed Coventry City in between my time at Rovers.

# MANAGERS - 1

*Match the manager with the period they were
in charge at Bristol Rovers*

| | | |
|---|---|---|
| 21. | **Gerry Francis** | *1980-81* |
| 22. | **Bobby Gould** | *1921-26* |
| 23. | **Terry Cooper** | *1930-36* |
| 24. | **Bert Tann** | *1993-96* |
| 25. | **Andy Wilson** | *1987-1991* |
| 26. | **John Ward** | *1926-29* |
| 27. | **Ian Holloway** | *1972-77* |
| 28. | **Don Megson** | *1981-83* |
| 29. | **Joe Palmer** | *1950-1968* |
| 30. | **Albert Prince-Cox** | *1996-2001* |

# STEVE WHITE

31. How many spells at Bristol Rovers did Steve have – 2, 3 or 4?

32. Where was Steve born in January 1959?

33. How many League goals did Steve score for Bristol Rovers in his career – 33, 44 or 55?

34. In what position did Steve play for Rovers?

35. How many League appearances did Steve make for the Pirates in his career – 151, 161 or 171?

36. Which Pirates boss brought Steve for his second spell at the club?

37. Following on from the previous question, how much did Bristol Rovers pay Charlton Athletic?

38. What is the name of Steve's son, who signed professional contracts in 2008 with Rovers?

39. Which club did Steve sign for in 1986?

40. Which team did Steve become the manager of in November 2003?

# CLUB HONOURS

*Match the honours with the season they achieved them*

| | | |
|---|---|---|
| 41. | League Cup Quarter-Finals | 2006/07 |
| 42. | Division Three Cup Winners | 1952/53 |
| 43. | League Two Play-off Winners | 1994/95 |
| 44. | Division Two Play-off Runners-up | 1989/90 |
| 45. | Watney Cup Winners | 1973/74 |
| 46. | Champions Division Three | 1957/58 |
| 47. | FA Cup Quarter-Finals | 1971/72 |
| 48. | Southern League Champions | 1971/72 |
| 49. | Division Three Runners-up | 1904/05 |
| 50. | Champions Division Three (South) | 1934/35 |

# DAVID MEHEW

**51.** In which year was David born in Camberley – 1965, 1966 or 1967?

**52.** Which club did David sign from to join Rovers in July 1985?

**53.** How many League appearances did David make for the Pirates?

**54.** How many Bristol Rovers goals did David score for Rovers during 1986/1987 in his 20 starts?

**55.** How many League goals did David score for Rovers in his career – 60, 63 or 66?

**56.** Which Cup Final did David play in for Rovers in 1990?

**57.** What was David's nickname at Bristol Rovers?

**58.** Which Midlands club did David play for during 1994/1995 making 13 appearances?

**59.** True or false: David was part of the Bristol Rovers team when the Pirates won the Third Division Championship in 1990?

**60.** Which manager handed David his Rovers debut?

# WHERE DID THEY GO? – 1

*Match the player with the club they went
to after leaving Bristol Rovers*

| | | |
|---|---|---|
| 61. | Junior Agogo | Watford |
| 62. | Nathan Ellington | Crystal Palace |
| 63. | Barry Hayles | Nottingham Forest |
| 64. | Jamie Cureton | Wigan Athletic |
| 65. | Gary Penrice | Chelsea |
| 66. | Scott Sinclair | Fulham |
| 67. | Tony Pounder | Cambridge United |
| 68. | Gareth Taylor | Weymouth |
| 69. | Devon White | Huddersfield Town |
| 70. | Marcus Stewart | Reading |

# 2008/2009

71. Which team beat Rovers 3-2 at home on the opening day of the season?

72. Which two Rovers players scored a brace in the 6-1 home win during August 2008?

73. Which Essex based team did Bristol Rovers beat 4-2 at home during October 2008?

74. Following on from the previous question, which midfielder scored all 4 goals for Rovers in the game?

75. Which forward scored Rovers equaliser in the 2-2 away draw against Yeovil Town during September 2008?

76. Who was manager of Bristol Rovers during this season?

77. Which forward signed from West Ham United in July 2008?

78. Which team beat Rovers 2-1 on 1 November 2008 by scoring two goals in the last 3 minutes after Jo Kuffour had put Rovers in front after 61 minutes?

79. Which team did Rovers beat 1-0 away from home whilst playing at the Weston Homes Community Stadium during October 2008?

80. Following on from the previous question, who scored the only goal for Rovers?

# KENNY HIBBITT

81. Kenny was born on 3 January in which year – 1949, 1951 or 1953?

82. Where was Kenny born – Bradford, Barnsley or Leeds?

83. How many years was Kenny at Wolverhampton Wanderers – 12, 14 or 16?

84. How many League Cups did Kenny win with Wolves?

85. In which year did Kenny transfer to Bristol Rovers – 1985, 1986 or 1987?

86. From which team did Rovers sign Kenny?

87. How many games did Kenny play in his two years at Bristol Rovers – 50, 53 or 56?

88. True or false: Kenny's career came to an end when he broke his leg playing for Rovers against Southend United in February 1988?

89. True or false: Kenny was assistant manager to Bobby Gould at the Pirates?

90. True or false: Kenny's older brother Terry use to play for Newcastle United?

# 2007/2008

91. Which team did Rovers draw 1-1 with on the opening day of the season with Andrew Williams scoring the Pirates' equaliser?

92. Who was the Rovers manager during this season?

93. Which team did Rovers beat 3-0 at home during December 2007?

94. Following on from the previous question, which three players scored the goals in the game?

95. True or false: Bristol Rovers were unbeaten in their first three League games during August 2007?

96. Who finished the club's highest scorer with 13 League goals in 46 games?

97. Who scored the winning goal, a penalty; in the 3-2 home win during February against Port Vale?

98. Which midfielder scored six League goals during this season?

99. Which defender signed from Hull City during January 2008?

100. True or false: Rovers lost their final three games of the season?

# NATIONALITIES - 1

*Match the player to their nationality*

| | | |
|---|---|---|
| 101. | Glyn Jones | Latvian |
| 102. | Guy Ipoua | Argentinean |
| 103. | Mickey Evans | Scottish |
| 104. | Vitalijs Astafjevs | French |
| 105. | Aidan McCaffrey | Cameroonian |
| 106. | Gino Padula | Irish |
| 107. | Scott Howie | English |
| 108. | Nigel Pierre | Welsh |
| 109. | Moussa Dagnogo | Italian |
| 110. | Giuliano Grazioli | Trinidad & Tobagonian |

# WHO AM I? – 2

111. I took the post of director of football in 2006. I managed Middlesbrough in the early 1990s and Luton Town between 1995 and 2000.

112. I am the goalkeeper who was banned in the early 1960s for accepting a bribe to throw a match.

113. I won nine Welsh caps during my playing career and took over as Rovers manager in 2005.

114. I was assigned from Swansea for £100,000, I am a centre forward and scored twice in my third League game for the club against Hereford in a 6-1 home win.

115. I am a goalkeeper and played 45 League games for Rovers during 2000/2001.

116. I signed from Norwich City in October 1996 having been on loan to Rovers for a month beforehand. I scored 72 League goals for Rovers in my career.

117. I am a defender, born in Wolverhampton in 1977. I came to the club in 2004 from Kidderminster.

118. I was born in Swindon in 1974. I am a defender who played for Rovers between January 1999 and March 2002.

119. I am a defender and scored one of Rovers goals in the 2-2 home draw during September 2007 against Nottingham Forest. That was my first goal for Rovers since joining the club in 2006.

120. I am a midfielder and had two spells at the club, 1984 to 1989 and then 1997 to 2000. I scored 61 League goals for the Pirates in my career.

# WHERE DID THEY COME FROM? – 1

*Match the player with the team they came from to join Bristol Rovers*

| | | |
|---|---|---|
| 121. | Craig Disley | Preston North End |
| 122. | Gerry Francis | Queens Park Rangers |
| 123. | Bobby Gould | Coventry City |
| 124. | Ian Holloway | Leeds United |
| 125. | Kenny Hibbitt | Mansfield Town |
| 126. | Geoff Twentyman | Wolverhampton Wanderers |
| 127. | Carl Saunders | Notts County |
| 128. | John Scales | Norwich City |
| 129. | David Pipe | Stoke City |
| 130. | Che Wilson | Portsmouth |

# LEAGUE DEBUTS

*Match the appropriate debut to the player*

| | | |
|---|---|---|
| *131.* | **Craig Disley** | **1-1 draw against Port Vale (away), August 2007** |
| *132.* | **Steve Elliott** | **1-1 draw against Brighton & Hove Albion (away), August 2008** |
| *133.* | **Matt Groves** | **2-0 defeat against Mansfield (away), August 2004** |
| *134.* | **David Pipe** | **1-1 draw against Port Vale (away), August 2007** |
| *135.* | **Charles Reece** | **2-0 defeat against Mansfield (away), August 2004** |
| *136.* | **Andrew Williams** | **2-0 defeat against Brighton & Hove Albion (home), April 2008** |
| *137.* | **Stuart Campbell** | **2-1 defeat against Huddersfield Town (away), December 2007** |
| *138.* | **Steve Phillips** | **4-2 defeat against Leyton Orient (away), September 2004** |
| *139.* | **Ben Hunt** | **3-0 win against Carlisle United (home), December 2007** |
| *140.* | **Charlie Clough** | **4-1 defeat against Peterborough United (away), August 2006** |

# ROVERS WINS IN LEAGUE DERBIES

*Match the result with the League and date
the match was played*

141. **Division Three (South)**
     **5 May 1936**                          *Rovers 5 – 1 City*

142. **Division Three (South)**
     **23 September 1922**                    *Rovers 2 – 0 City*

143. **League Two**
     **22 April 2000**                        *City 1 – 2 Rovers*

144. **Division One**
     **13 December 1992**                     *Rovers 3 – 1 City*

145. **Division Three**
     **12 April 1982**                        *Rovers 1 – 0 City*

146. **Division Three (South)**
     **30 December 1950**                     *City 0 – 2 Rovers*

147. **Division Three (South)**
     **30 December 1933**                     *Rovers 3 – 0 City*

148. **Division Three (South)**
     **7 September 1935**                     *Rovers 2 –1 City*

149. **Division Three**
     **2 May 1990**                           *Rovers 4 – 0 City*

150. **Division Three**
     **12 April 1988**                        *City 0 – 1 Rovers*

# MATCH THE YEAR – 1

*Match the year to the event*

| | | |
|---|---|---|
| 151. | Finished runners-up of the Football League Trophy | 1991 |
| 152. | Club moved to Twerton Park | 1998 |
| 153. | Paul Trollope takes over as Pirates manager | 1986 |
| 154. | Club formed Bristol Rovers ladies team | 1954 |
| 155. | Fulham pay £2.1 million for Barry Hayles | 2007 |
| 156. | Bristol Rovers beat Shrewsbury Town 7-0 in Division Three | 1952 |
| 157. | Ian Halloway takes over as Rovers manager | 1964 |
| 158. | Bristol Rovers beat Swansea City 7-0 in Division Two | 2005 |
| 159. | Rovers beat Brighton & Hove Albion 7-0 in Division Three South | 1996 |
| 160. | Gerry Francis left Rovers as manager | 1998 |

# IAN HOLLOWAY

161. Ian was born on 12 March in which year – 1961, 1963 or 1965?

162. Where was Ian born – Bristol, Plymouth or Swindon?

163. Ian started his professional career in 1981 with which club?

164. True or false: Ian had three spells at Bristol Rovers, two as a player and one as manager?

165. How many League appearances did Ian make for Rovers in his playing career – 379, 389 or 399?

166. True or false: Ian was in the same class at school as fellow Rovers player Gary Penrice?

167. In August 1991 which club did Ian sign with for £230,000?

168. Which club was Ian manager of in the 2006/07 season?

169. On 22 November 2007 Ian became manager of Leicester City. Who were Leicester's very first opponents whom they beat 2-0?

170. True or false:  In June 2004 Ian took part in the BBC series Stress Test?

# 2006/2007

171. In which position did the club finish in the League?

172. Rovers' first League win came in the third game of the season, against which team in a 1-0 home win with Andy Sandell scoring?

173. Who was Rovers manager during this season?

174. Which player scored a brace in the 4-0 home win against Accrington Stanley during December 2006?

175. How much did Bristol Rovers pay Rochdale for Rickie Lambert in August 2006?

176. Who scored a last minute winner in the 3-2 home win against Peterborough United during February 2007?

177. Who was the club's highest League scorer with goals in 46 appearances?

178. Which midfielder scored a brace in the 2-0 home win against Bury during April 2007?

179. How many League games did the club win in their 46 League matches?

180. Which team did Rovers beat 2-1 away on the final day of the season?

# GERRY FRANCIS

181.    Gerry was born on 6 December in which year –
        1951, 1953 or 1955?

182.    Where was Gerry born – Chiswick, Kew or Putney?

183.    For which club did Gerry start his professional career in
        1968 where he stayed eleven years?

184.    From 1974 to 1976 Gerry played for England at
        international level, how many times did he play for
        them – 10, 12 or 14?

185.    Gerry Captained England on how many occasions –
        6, 8 or 10?

186.    Who appointed Gerry as England captain in 1975?

187.    In 1985 from which club did Bristol Rovers sign Gerry?

188.    True or false: In 1987 he became player/manager of
        Rovers putting £20,000 of his own money into the
        club?

189.    In 1990 Gerry guided Rovers to the Leyland DAF Cup
        Final, whom did they lose to in the final?

190.    In which year did Gerry finish in Football management
        – 2000, 2001 or 2002?

# PLAY-OFF FINAL WINNERS – 2007

191.    Where was the final played?

192.    What was the score in the final?

193.    Which team did Rovers beat in the final?

194.    Can you name the Rovers players who scored in the final?

195.    Which team did Bristol Rovers beat in the semi-final?

196.    Following on from the previous questions, what was the aggregate score after playing them home and away?

197.    Who scored the winning goal in 2-1 home win, first leg semi final?

198.    What was the attendance at the final – 41,589, 51,589 or 61,589?

199.    Can you name seven of the starting 11 who started in the final?

200.    Can you name the only substitute that the Pirates used in the game, coming on in the 64th minute for Lewis Haldene?

# BOBBY GOULD

201. Bobby was born on 12 June in which year – 1942, 1944 or 1946?

202. Where was Bobby born – Coventry, Birmingham or Nottingham?

203. Bobby signed for Bristol Rovers in October 1977 for what fee - £10,000, £15,000 or £20,000?

204. How many League goals did Bobby score in his 36 League matches for the Pirates – 10, 12 or 14?

205. Who was Bobby assistant manager to when he joined Chelsea in 1979?

206. Bobby took Wimbledon to the FA Cup final in 1988, whom did they beat 1-0 with Larry Sanchez scoring to lift the trophy?

207. Which national team was Bobby manager of from 1995 to 1999?

208. Following on from the previous question, Bobby's last game in charge of the national team resulted in a 4-0 defeat to which country?

209. True or false: In 2006 Bobby assisted his son Jonathan managing Hawke's Bay United in Australia?

210. True or false: Bobby's other son Richard is Chief Executive of Somerset County Cricket Club?

# MARCUS BROWNING

211. In which year was Marcus born in Bristol?

212. In which position did Marcus play whilst at Rovers?

213. Who scored the other goal when Marcus scored in the 2-0 home win against Shrewsbury Town during February 1997 in the League?

214. How many League goals has Marcus scored for Rovers in his career – 3, 13 or 31?

215. How many League goals did Marcus score for Rovers during 1996/1997?

216. What team did Marcus play for between August 2002 and July 2007?

217. How many League games did Marcus play for Rovers in his career?

218. When Marcus left Rovers, which team did he join in February 1997 costing them £450,000?

219. Marcus is a full international for which country?

220. Following on from the previous question, how many international caps did Marcus win whilst at Rovers?

# TONY PULIS

221. Tony was born on 16 January in which year – 1958, 1960 or 1962?

222. What nationality is Tony – English, Welsh or Irish?

223. Tony started his professional playing career at which club in 1975?

224. Tony is one of the youngest professional players ever to obtain his FA coaching badge, at what age did he obtain this – 19, 21 or 23?

225. True or false: Tony was Harry Redknapp's assistant at AFC Bournemouth?

226. In two playing spells for Rovers how many years did Tony stay with the club – 6, 8 or 10?

227. How many League appearances did Tony make for The Gas – 120, 125 or 130?

228. Which team did Tony manage between 1995 and 1999?

229. True or false: Tony was voted manager of the month for Stoke City in March 2007?

230. For which team, as manager, did Tony win automatic promotion into the Premiership in May 2008?

# HARRY BAMFORD

231. In which position did Harry play during his playing days?

232. Which honour did Harry win during his time at Bristol Rovers?

233. In which year did Harry sadly pass away due to a motorcycle accident – 1950, 1954 or 1958?

234. Following on from the previous question, Rovers and City formed a team to play a testimonial for Harry against which top-flight London club?

235. In which year was Harry born in Bristol?

236. How many League games did Harry play for Rovers – 286, 386 or 486?

237. How many goals did Harry score in his 38 FA Cup appearances for Rovers?

238. Which manager handed Harry his Pirates debut?

239. How many League goals did Harry score for Rovers during his career?

240. Apart from the manager in question 238, which other manager did Harry play under at Bristol Rovers?

# WHERE DID THEY GO? – 2

*Match the player with the club they went to
after leaving Bristol Rovers*

| | | |
|---|---|---|
| 241. | Lee Thorpe | Crystal Palace |
| 242. | Adam Barrett | Torquay United |
| 243. | Marcus Browning | Tottenham Hotspur |
| 244. | Gary Mabbutt | Swansea City |
| 245. | Nigel Martyn | Halifax Town |
| 246. | Mick Channon | Doncaster Rovers |
| 247. | Paul Handrie | Huddersfield Town |
| 248. | Brian Parkin | Southend United |
| 249. | Darren Mullings | Norwich City |
| 250. | Steve Foster | Wycombe Wanderers |

# 1990s

251. **Which two players did the club sign from Portsmouth during February 1999?**

252. **In what position in the League did Rovers finish during 1998/1999 – 3rd, 13th or 23rd?**

253. **Who was Rovers manager between August 1993 and May 1996?**

254. **Which striker did the club sell to Huddersfield for £1.2 million during July 1996?**

255. **In what position in the League did Rovers finish during 1994/1995 – 4th, 14th or 24th?**

256. **Who was Rovers manager between August 1992 and March 1993?**

257. **Which London team did Rovers beat 3-0 away in the League on the last day of the 1992/1993 season?**

258. **In what position in the League did Rovers finish during 1991/1992 – 3rd, 13th or 23rd?**

259. **Which defender did the club sign from Stoke City during September 1993?**

260. **Who left the club in November 1993 for Hereford, having made over 200 League appearances for the club, scoring 17 goals?**

# WHERE DID THEY COME FROM? – 2

*Match the player to the club they joined Bristol Rovers from*

| | | |
|---|---|---|
| 261. | Richard Walker | Hull City |
| 262. | Tony Sealy | Derby County |
| 263. | Julian Alsop | Stockport County |
| 264. | Aaron Lescott | Blackpool |
| 265. | Paul Hardyman | Queens Park Rangers |
| 266. | Danny Coles | Swindon Town |
| 267. | Terry Cooper | Reading |
| 268. | Scott Howie | Sunderland |
| 269. | Aidan McCaffrey | Bristol City |
| 270. | Matthew Lockwood | Halesowen Town |

# 2005/2006

271. Who started the season as manager of Rovers and left in September 2005?

272. Following on from the previous question, who took over in September 2005 as Pirates manager?

273. In what position did the club finish in the League?

274. Which goalkeeper did Bristol Rovers sign from Coventry City at the end of July 2005?

275. Which London team did Bristol Rovers draw 3-3 with at home during January 2006?

276. Who finished the club's highest League scorer with 20 goals in 46 games?

277. Following on from the previous question, which other Rovers player finished with double figures with 16 goals in his 42 appearances?

278. Who scored both goals for Rovers on Boxing Day 2005 in the 2-1 home win against Shrewsbury Town?

279. How many League games did the club win during their 46 matches?

280. Who scored the only goal in the 1-0 home win against Darlington during September 2005?

# JAMIE CURETON

281. Jamie was born 28 August in which year – 1975, 1977 or 1979?

282. Where was Jamie born – Bath, Weston-super-Mare or Bristol?

283. At which club did Jamie start his professional career in 1993?

284. In 1996 Jamie transferred to Bristol Rovers and stayed until 2000, how many League appearances did he make for them – 160, 165 or 170?

285. How many League goals did Jamie score for the Pirates – 70, 72 or 74?

286. Which club signed Jamie from Bristol Rovers in 2000?

287. In 2003/04 Jamie played 21 games for Busan I'Cons, in which Country?

288. In 2006/07 Jamie played for Colchester United, in this season he scored two hat-tricks against which two clubs?

289. True or false: Jamie won the Championship Golden Boot award with twenty-three goals as the League's top scorer in 2006/07 season?

290. On 29 June 2007 he moved back to Norwich City, to replace which striker who went to Derby County?

# 2004/2005

291.  Who managed the club during this season?

292.  True or false: Bristol Rovers won all four League matches during December 2004?

293.  Which team did Rovers beat on the opening day of the season away from home with Junior Agogo scoring a brace?

294.  Which midfielder signed in August 2004 from Stockport County?

295.  Who finished the club's highest League scorer with 19 goals?

296.  How many of the clubs 46 League games did they draw – 11, 21 or 31?

297.  In which position did the club finish in the League – 11th, 12th or 13th?

298.  Who scored the only goal in the 1-0 home win on the last day of the season against Wycombe Wanderers?

299.  Which striker scored 10 goals in 27 League appearances during this season?

300.  Which team did Rovers draw 4-4 with at home during March 2005, having been 4-2 down after 68 minutes?

# POSITIONS IN LEAGUE TWO

*Match the position Bristol Rovers finished in with the season*

| | | | |
|---|---|---|---|
| 301. | 1996/97 | 56 points | 7th |
| 302. | 2005/06 | 60 points | 10th |
| 303. | 1993/94 | 70 points | 17th |
| 304. | 1999/2000 | 80 points | 4th |
| 305. | 2006/07 | 72 points | 12th |
| 306. | 2000/01 | 51 points | 5th |
| 307. | 1994/95 | 82 points | 8th |
| 308. | 1998/99 | 56 points | 21st |
| 309. | 1995/96 | 70 points | 6th |
| 310. | 1997/98 | 70 points | 13th |

# PETER AITKEN

311. Where was Peter born in 1954?

312. In which position did Peter play during his playing days?

313. Which three managers did Peter play under during the 1970s whilst at Bristol Rovers?

314. How many League goals did Peter score for Rovers in his career?

315. What nationality is Peter?

316. How many League Cup goals did Peter score in his 13 appearances whilst playing for Rovers?

317. Which team did Peter play for during 1981/1982 making 18 appearances and scoring twice?

318. How many League appearances did Peter make in his Rovers career – 134, 234 or 334?

319. Which team did Peter join when he left the Pirates?

320. In 2005 which role at the club did Peter take up?

# POSITIONS IN LEAGUE THREE AND ENGLISH THIRD DIVISION

*Match the position Bristol Rovers finished in with the season*

| | | | |
|---|---|---|---|
| 321. | 1969/70 | 56 points | 16th |
| 322. | 2002/03 | 51 points | 7th |
| 323. | 1989/90 | 93 points | 15th |
| 324. | 1962/63 | 41 points | 3rd |
| 325. | 1982/83 | 75 points | 20th |
| 326. | 2001/02 | 45 points | 5th |
| 327. | 1985/86 | 54 points | 19th |
| 328. | 1966/67 | 53 points | 2nd |
| 329. | 2003/04 | 55 points | 23rd |
| 330. | 1973/74 | 61 points | 1st |

# MATCH THE YEAR – 2

*Match the year to the event*

| | | |
|---|---|---|
| 331. | Malcolm Allison leaves Rovers as manager | 1996 |
| 332. | The club were formed as Black Arabs FC | 1981 |
| 333. | Finished runners-up of the Football League Trophy | 1985 |
| 334. | The Club reached the FA Cup quarter finals for the first time since 1958 | 1883 |
| 335. | Team worn pink shirts in a friendly against Plymouth Argyle | 1993 |
| 336. | The Club moved to Eastville Stadium | 1990 |
| 337. | Bobby Gould takes over as manager (second spell) | 1990 |
| 338. | The Club won the Third Division title | 2006 |
| 339. | Ron Gingell took over as manager, managing them for one game | 1897 |
| 340. | The club moved to the Memorial Ground | 2008 |

# NATIONALITIES – 2

*Match the player to their nationality*

| | | |
|---|---|---|
| 341. | Joe Jacobson | French |
| 342. | Ciaran Toner | Ghanaian |
| 343. | Marcus Andreasson | Scottish |
| 344. | Michele Di Piedi | Irish |
| 345. | Stephane Leoni | Jamaican |
| 346. | Alistair Gibb | Swedish |
| 347. | Sam Oji | Welsh |
| 348. | Sandy McCubbin | Nigerian |
| 349. | Barry Hayles | Italian |
| 350. | Junior Agogo | English |

# 2003/2004

351.   Which team did Bristol Rovers beat 4-0 away during October 2003 with Andy Rammell scoring twice?

352.   In which position did the club finish in the League?

353.   Who finished the club's top goal scorer with 12 goals in 33 appearances?

354.   How many of the club's 46 League matches did Rovers win – 14, 20 or 26?

355.   Who scored the winning goal in the 85th minute on the opening day of the season against Scunthorpe United in the 2-1 away win?

356.   How many managers did Rovers have during this season?

357.   Following on from the previous question, can you name three of them?

358.   Who did Rovers sign from Stockport County during March 2004?

359.   Can you name the three goal scorers who scored against York City in the 3-1 home win against March 2004?

360.   Who scored a brace against Lincoln in the 3-1 home win during May 2004?

# NIGEL MARTYN

361. Nigel was born on 11 August in which year – 1964, 1966 or 1968?

362. Where was Nigel born, Newquay, Redruth or St. Austell?

363. In which position did Nigel play until he was 16?

364. At which club did Nigel start his amateur football career in 1983?

365. Nigel started his professional career at Bristol Rovers in 1987, how many League appearances did he make for the club?

366. True or false: He was the first goalkeeper in England to transfer for £1 million?

367. Which club signed Nigel from Rovers in 1989?

368. In Nigel's League career he played seven seasons at which two clubs?

369. Nigel made his international debut away for England in 1992, who were the opponents?

370. How many international appearances did Nigel make for his Country – 17, 23 or 29?

# IAN ALEXANDER

371. Where was Ian born in 1963 – Manchester, Glasgow or Cardiff?

372. Which manager signed Ian for Bristol Rovers?

373. How many League goals did Ian score for Bristol Rovers in his career – 6, 16 or 61?

374. What was Ian's nickname whilst playing for the Pirates?

375. How many League games did Ian play for Rovers in his career?

376. True or false: Ian was sent-off six times during his Rovers career?

377. Following on from the previous question, can you name the team Bristol Rovers were playing when Ian got sent-off three times?

378. In which year did Ian join the Pirates?

379. Ian took over as Rovers goalkeeper from Brian Parkin during 1991 and saved a penalty against which team?

380. When Ian left Rovers, which team did he take over as manager with Phil Purnell his assistant?

# GARY PENRICE

381. Gary was born on 23 March in which year – 1964, 1966 or 1968?

382. Where was Gary born – Bristol, Bath or Yeovil?

383. Which club said: "Gary will never make it as a professional footballer because he is too small," releasing him as an apprentice?

384. Which local team in the Bristol area did Gary first sign for?

385. Before Gary became a professional player, what was his trade?

386. In which year did Gary sign for Bristol Rovers?

387. In Gary's nine years at the club how many League appearances did Gary make for the Pirates – 230, 234 or 238?

388. How many League goals did Gary score for The Gas?

389. In 1989 which club did Gary sign for a club record of £500,000?

390. True or false: Gary now works as Head of Recruitment for Plymouth Argyle?

# 2002/2003

391. Which team did Rovers beat 3-1 at home in their fifth League game of the season, which was also the club's first win of the season?

392. Which striker signed from Swindon Town during July 2002?

393. In which position did Rovers finish in the League - 2nd, 12th or 20th?

394. Who was the Pirates manager during this season?

395. Who was the club's highest League scorer with 11 goals in 34 appearances?

396. Which team did Rovers beat 5-2 away during September 2002?

397. Following on from the previous question, who scored a hat-trick in the games?

398. From which club did Rovers sign Graham Hyde in November 2002?

399. Which forward scored the only goal in the 1-0 away win against Oxford United during April 2003?

400. Who scored a brace in the 3-1 home win against Cambridge during April 2003?

# SQUAD NUMBERS - 1
## 2008-2009

*Match the player with their Bristol Rovers squad number*

| | | |
|---|---|---|
| 401. | Rickie Lambert | 32 |
| 402. | Craig Disley | 2 |
| 403. | Steve Phillips | 33 |
| 404. | Aaron Lescott | 9 |
| 405. | Steve Elliott | 16 |
| 406. | Danny Coles | 4 |
| 407. | Darryl Duffy | 6 |
| 408. | Ryan Green | 1 |
| 409. | Steve Book | 10 |
| 410. | Chris Lines | 20 |

# 1980s

411. Which defender signed from Bournemouth in October 1987?

412. In which position did the club finish in the League during 1987/1988?

413. Who took over as manager in July 1987 and was boss until May 1991?

414. In which position did the club finish in the League during 1983/1984?

415. How many spells at the club did Ian Holloway have during the 1980s at Bristol Rovers?

416. How many goals did Mark Hughes score in his Bristol Rovers career during the 1980s?

417. In which year did Mark O'Connor sign for the club from Queens Park Rangers?

418. In which position did the club finish in the League during 1981/1982?

419. Which team did Keith Curle sign for during November 1983 when he left the club?

420. Which defender played for Rovers between 1985 and 1987 and then went on to play for Wimbledon, Liverpool and Tottenham?

# BRISTOL CUP/TROPHY DERBIES

*Match the result with the cup/date*

| | | |
|---|---|---|
| 421. | FA Cup 10 December 1983 | City 1 – 3 Rovers |
| 422. | FA Cup 15 February 1958 | City 3 – 0 Rovers |
| 423. | FA Cup 27 January 1968 | City 0 – 0 Rovers |
| 424. | FA Cup 8 December 1945 | Rovers 1 –2 City |
| 425. | League Cup 8 October 1991 | City 4 – 2 Rovers |
| 426. | FA Cup 8 December 1984 | City 3 – 4 Rovers |
| 427. | FA Cup 10 January 1925 | Rovers 1 – 0 City |
| 428. | Johnstone's Paint Trophy 27 February 2007 | City 2 – 4 Rovers |
| 429. | LDV Vans Trophy 9 January 2002 | Rovers 0 – 1 City |
| 430. | League Cup 12 August 1997 | City 0 – 0 Rovers |

# GERAINT WILLIAMS

431. In which year was Geraint born – 1961, 1962 or 1963?

432. How many League goals did Geraint score for Rovers in his career?

433. Which Welsh based team did Geraint support as a young boy?

434. What is Geraint's real first name (as Geraint is really his middle name)?

435. Can you name the two East Anglian teams that Geraint played for during his playing career?

436. Against which team did Geraint make his Bristol Rovers debut?

437. How many full Welsh international caps did Geraint win for his country?

438. In which position did Geraint play during his playing days?

439. How many League games did Geraint play in his Rovers career?

440. When Geraint left Rovers in 1985 which team did he join?

# CLUB RECORDS

441. Bristol Rovers had three record League wins all at home; Brighton & Hove Albion, Swansea City and Shrewsbury Town, what was the score?

442. What is Rovers record FA cup qualifying score against Weymouth Town on 17 November 1900?

443. What is Rovers record FA cup proper score, which occurred in Round One 14 November 1987 against Merthyr Tydfil?

444. The Pirates record defeat was 0-12 and occurred in the Division Three (South) 13 April 1936, who were their opponents?

445. In the League Division Three (South) season of 1952/53 who was the record scorer with 33 League goals?

446. Stuart Taylor made the most Bristol Rovers League appearances from 1966 to 1980, how many did he make – 526, 546 or 566?

447. From 1949 to 1964 Geoff Bradford holds the record for scoring the most career League goals for Rovers, how many?

448. The record transfer fee of £370,000 was paid for Andy Tillson in 1992, from which club did he come from?

449. The record transfer fee received by Rovers is £2 million for Barry Hayles and Jason Roberts, which two clubs did they join?

450. In the League Division Three (South) 1952/53 season Rovers scored how many League goals?

# 1970s

451. In which year was Vitalijs Astafjevs born – 1969, 1970 or 1971?

452. In which position did the club finish in the League during 1978/1979?

453. Can you name the two years that the club made it to the quarter finals of the League Cup during the 1970s?

454. Who managed the Pirates between 1972 and 1977?

455. In which position did the club finish in the League during 1973/1974?

456. Which Division did the club play in between 1974 and 1981?

457. Can you name the two years that Rovers won the Gloucestershire Cup during the 1970s?

458. In which position did the club finish in the League during 1975/1976?

459. During 1973/1974 Rovers beat which team 8-2 away from home?

460. Following on from the previous question, which two Rovers players scored hat-tricks in the game?

# SQUAD NUMBERS – 2
## 2008-2009

*Match the player with their Bristol Rovers squad number*

461. **Tom Parrinello**            *11*

462. **Joe Jacobson**             *23*

463. **Alex Kite**                *21*

464. **Andrew Williams**          *7*

465. **Craig Hinton**             *13*

466. **Jeff Hughes**              *8*

467. **David Pipe**               *24*

468. **Ryan Paddock**             *5*

469. **Stuart Campbell**          *3*

470. **Mike Green**               *14*

# 2001/2002

471. Who scored the only goal in the 79th minute during the 1-0 home League win on the opening day of the season against Torquay United?

472. Who started the season as manager and then left on Christmas Eve?

473. True or false: Rovers failed to win a League match during October 2001?

474. In what position in the League did Rovers finish – 3rd, 13th or 23rd?

475. Which striker finished the season as the club's top League scorer with 15 goals in 27 games?

476. Who scored a hat-trick in the 4-1 home win against Swansea during January 2002?

477. Which Dutch forward did Rovers sign in November 2001 from KR Reykjavik?

478. Which London team did Bristol Rovers beat 5-3 at home on Boxing Day 2001?

479. Following on from the previous season, who scored a hat-trick in the game for Rovers?

480. Which Irish midfielder did Rovers sign from Crystal Palace in March 2002?

# STUART TAYLOR

481.  In which year was Stuart born – 1946, 1947 or 1948?

482.  In which position did Stuart play during his playing days?

483.  True or false: Stuart was a one man club and played at Rovers during his entire playing career?

484.  What record does Stuart hold at Bristol Rovers?

485.  Which manager handed Stuart his debut at Rovers?

486.  How many League goals did Stuart score for Rovers in his career – 20, 28 or 36?

487.  True or false: Stuart managed Bristol Rovers in 1992?

488.  How many League games did Stuart play for Rovers in his career – 346, 446 or 546?

489.  In which year did Stuart play his last Rovers game and hang his boots up, ending his 15 year playing career at the club?

490.  Which manager did Stuart play under between 1972 and 1977?

# JIM EADIE

491. In what year was Jim born in Kirkintilloch?

492. How many League appearances did Jim make for Bristol Rovers in his career – 103, 143 or 183?

493. Which position did Jim play in his playing days?

494. What was Jim's nickname whilst playing for the Pirates?

495. Which honour did Jim win whilst at Bristol Rovers during 1973/1974?

496. From which Welsh based team did Jim join Rovers in 1973?

497. True or false: during Jim's career at Bristol Rovers he once went nearly 700 minutes without conceding a goal?

498. What nationality is Jim – English, Scottish or Welsh?

499. When Jim left the Pirates which team did he join?

500. In which year did Jim leave Eastville Park?

# BRUCE BANNISTER

501. Bruce was born on 14 April in which year – 1945, 1947 or 1949?

502. Where was Bruce born – Bradford, Bristol or Brighton?

503. Rovers paid £23,000 for Bruce in November 1971 from which club did he sign?

504. What was the Bruce Bannister and Alan Warboys striking partnership called?

505. How many League appearances did Bruce make for the Pirates – 200, 202 or 204?

506. How many League goals did Bruce score in his time with Rovers?

507. For which club did Bruce sign in 1976?

508. Did Bruce ever play in the English First Division – yes or no?

509. True or false: Bruce was an active worker for the Players Union?

510. At which club did Bruce end his playing career in 1982?

# UNUSUAL RESULTS

*Match the clubs unusual result to the match played*

511.  v. Lincoln City (away),
      Play-off semi-final, May 2007                    3-3

512.  v. Colchester United (away),
      League, January 2000                             3-4

513.  v. Walsall (home),
      League, October 1998                             3-3

514.  v. Mansfield Town (home),
      League, March 2005                               5-3

515.  v. Doncaster Rovers (away),
      League, October 2003                             6-2

516.  v. Shrewsbury Town (away),
      League, September 2002                           1-5

517.  v. Mansfield Town (away),
      League, December 2005                            4-3

518.  v. Oxford United (home),
      League, April 2001                               5-2

519.  v. Macclesfield Town (away),
      League, May 1999                                 4-5

520.  v. Luton Town (home),
      League, September 2000                           4-4

# PETER BEADLE

521. Peter was born on 13 May in which year – 1972, 1974 or 1976?

522. Where was Peter born – Southwark, Shepherds Bush or Lambeth?

523. Which team did Peter sign from, to replace Gareth Taylor who had left to join Crystal Palace?

524. Peter scored his first League hat-trick in ten minutes against which team?

525. How many League appearances did Peter make for The Gas – 93, 98 or 103?

526. Which team did Peter join in 1998?

527. True or false: Peter went on to play for Bristol City where he picked up a winners' medal for winning the LDV Vans Trophy in 2003?

528. In 2003 Peter had a brief spell at Brentford where, on his debut, he was sent off and he never played for Brentford again, how many minutes into his debut was he sent off?

529. In June 2004 Peter moved to Bath to become player/manager of which West Country non-League team?

530. True or false: On 27 April 2008 Eastbourne Borough sacked Peter for failing to make the play-offs?

# 2000/2001

531.    Which team did Rovers beat 3-0 away during September 2000 with Simon Bryant, Micky Evans and Scott Jones scoring?

532.    Which manager started the season and then left at the end of January 2001?

533.    Following on from the previous question, can you name the two people who took over at the club until the end of the season?

534.    Which Irish forward did Rovers sign from West Bromwich Albion in September 2000 for £250,000?

535.    Can you name the club's highest scorer with 15 goals in 42 appearances?

536.    How much did Rovers sell Andy Tillson to Walsall for during August 2000?

537.    Which Essex based team did Rovers beat 2-0 at home during April 2001 with Vitaly Astafjevs and Nathan Ellington scoring in the last five minutes?

538.    In which position did the club finish in the League?

539.    Who scored a brace for the Pirates in the 6-2 away win against Brentford in August 2000?

540.    Which team did Rovers beat 4-0 at home on the final day of the season with Mark Walters (2), Richie Partridge and Nathan Ellington scoring?

# ALFIE BIGGS

541.   Alfie was born on 8 February in which year – 1932, 1934 or 1936?

542.   Where was Alfie born – Minehead, Bristol or Weston-super-Mare?

543.   Between Alfie's two spells at Rovers, which club did he play for, for fifteen months who were managed by Jimmy Milne?

544.   In the 1963/64 season how many League goals did Alfie score - a club record?

545.   How many League appearances did Alfie make for Rovers – 404, 414 or 424?

546.   How many League goals did Alfie score in his career with Rovers?

547.   In a 1956 FA Cup match Alfie scored a brace in the 4-0 home win against whom?

548.   Which two striking partners did Alfie play with while at the Pirates?

549.   In the 1967/68 season which team was Alfie transferred to?

550.   True or false: In 1953 Alfie was due to sign for rivals Bristol City, but he was kept waiting so he went instead to Eastville and signed for Rovers?

# BIG WINS

*Match the big win with the team they beat in the season*

| | | |
|---|---|---|
| **551.** | ***v. Chester City (home), League, December 2004*** | **5-0** |
| **552.** | ***v. Hereford United (home), League, August 2008*** | **5-0** |
| **553.** | ***v. Rushden & Diamonds (home), FA Cup 2nd round, December 2007*** | **4-0** |
| **554.** | ***v. Accrington Stanley (home), League, December 2006*** | **5-2** |
| **555.** | ***v. Bournemouth (home), League, December 1997*** | **4-1** |
| **556.** | ***v. Bath City (away), FA Cup 1st round, November 1994*** | **4-0** |
| **557.** | ***v. Barnet (home), League, March 1994*** | **6-1** |
| **558.** | ***v. Brentford (away), League, September 2000*** | **6-2** |
| **559.** | ***v. Bristol City (home), League, December 1992*** | **5-1** |
| **560.** | ***v. Exeter City (home), FA Cup 2nd round, December 1998*** | **5-3** |

# GEOFF BRADFORD

561. Geoff was born on 18 July in which year – 1925, 1927 or 1929?

562. Geoff first played for which non-League Bristol team, where he was discovered by Rovers in 1945?

563. Geoff made his Rovers debut on 24 September 1949 in a 1-0 defeat, against whom?

564. What was Geoff's nickname at Rovers because he was known for his sleeping before games?

565. True or false: In 1961 Rovers turned down an offer from Bill Shankly, which would have seen him play for Liverpool?

566. How many League appearances did Geoff make for Rovers?

567. How many League goals did Geoff score for The Gas – 242, 244 or 246?

568. What happened to Geoff on 2 October 1955, and was never to happen again?

569. In 1955 Geoff scored the fifth goal in a 5-1 friendly win for England against which team?

570. True or false: Geoff is only one of two players to rep resent England from Bristol Rovers?

# 1960s

571.  Can you name the three managers that Rovers had during the 1960s?

572.  In which position did Rovers finish in the League during 1968/1969?

573.  In which year were the Pirates relegated to Division Three?

574.  Which Division did the club play in from 1962 to 1974?

575.  In which position did Rovers finish in the League during 1964/1965?

576.  What kind of shirts did Rovers play in during 1962/1963 – all blue, blue pinstripes or blue and white quarters?

577.  In August 1960, Rovers were losing a match 4-0 to Leeds United at half time, what was the score after 90 minutes?

578.  In which position did Rovers finish in the League during 1962/1963 – 17th, 19th or 21st?

579.  For which cup was Rovers in the final in 1963, 1965 and 1966?

580.  Which team did Geoff Bradford score his first goal against for the club in a 4-0 win during December 1963?

# TOP GOALSCORERS

*Match the players to the number of goals they scored*

| | | |
|---|---|---|
| 581. | Harold Jarman | 110 |
| 582. | Bruce Bannister | 92 |
| 583. | Alfie Biggs | 143 |
| 584. | Geoff Bradford | 133 |
| 585. | Peter Hooper | 96 |
| 586. | Bobby Jones | 197 |
| 587. | Vic Lambden | 260 |
| 588. | George Petherbridge | 106 |
| 589. | Paul Randall | 107 |
| 590. | Dai Ward | 93 |

# POT LUCK – 1

591. In which year did Rovers win the Watney Cup?

592. The record attendance at the Memorial Stadium was 11,433 against which team in the League Cup during October 2000?

593. How many League goals did Devon White score for the pirates in his 202 League appearances for Rovers – 33, 43 or 53?

594. In which year did the club first play football in League One?

595. How many League appearances did Dick Sheppard make for the Pirates during his Rovers career – 51, 151 or 251?

596. In which season did Rovers win the Football League Third Division South Cup?

597. Why is one of the club's nicknames The Gas?

598. Which song is sung in support of the team, which was written by Leadbelly?

599. What is the club's postcode at the Memorial Ground?

600. How much did the club pay Queens Park Rangers for Andy Tillson in November 1992 which was a club record?

# YEARS AT THE CLUB

*Match the player with the seasons they spent at Bristol Rovers*

601.   Phil Bater                1987-1992

602.   Brian Parkin              1965-1980

603.   Harold Jarman             1945-1955

604.   Kenny Stephens            1959-1973

605.   Andy Tillson              1974-1981

606.   Jason Roberts             1992-2000

607.   Devon White               1989-1996

608.   Steve White               1998-2000

609.   Stuart Taylor             1977-1980

610.   Vic Lambden               1970-1978

# LEAGUE GOALSCORERS – 1

*Match the number of league goals they scored
for the club against the player*

| | | |
|---|---|---|
| 611. | Larry Lloyd | 101 |
| 612. | Bruce Bannister | 127 |
| 613. | Wayne Jones | 80 |
| 614. | Harold Jarman | 1 |
| 615. | Geoff Bradford | 12 |
| 616. | Ray Mabbutt | 16 |
| 617. | Vitalijs Astafjevs | 242 |
| 618. | Peter Hooper | 27 |
| 619. | Barry Hayles | 28 |
| 620. | Vaughan Jones | 32 |

# TOP APPEARANCES

*Match the player with the total number of League and cup appearances they made for Bristol Rovers*

621.  Harold Bamford                463

622.  Ian Holloway                  511

623.  George Petherbridge           502(11)

624.  Ray Warren                    627

625.  Vaughan Jones                 524

626.  Alfie Biggs                   453(18)

627.  Stuart Taylor                 461(12)

628.  Geoff Bradford                486

629.  Harold Jarman                 437(14)

630.  Bobby Jones                   496

# 1950s

631. Who took over as manager on New Year's day 1950 and went on to manage the club for the whole decade?

632. In which position did Rovers finish in the League during 1957/1958?

633. Who scored a club record 33 League goals during 1952/1953 in Division Three South?

634. Which top-flight team did Rovers beat 4-0 in the FA Cup during January 1956?

635. In which position did Rovers finish in the League during 1950/1951 – 5th, 6th or 7th?

636. Which League did Bristol Rovers play in between 1953 and 1962?

637. Which season were the club Division Three (South) Champions during the 1950s?

638. How many England caps did Geoff Bradford win whilst at Rovers, scoring one international goal?

639. In which position did Rovers finish in the League during 1954/1955?

640. In which two years during the 1950s did the club make the FA Cup quarter finals?

# HAROLD JARMAN

641. Harold was born on 4 May in which year – 1937, 1939 or 1941?

642. In which West Country city was Harold born?

643. In which year did Harold join Bristol Rovers – 1955, 1957 or 1959?

644. In Harold's fourteen years at Rovers, how many League appearances did he make?

645. How many League goals did Harold score at the Pirates – 127, 130 or 133?

646. When Harold left Rovers in 1973, which club did he join?

647. Harold finished his football career playing for which USA team?

648. Following on from the above question, when Harold finally hung up his boots in the USA, which famous World Cup player replaced him?

649. Which other sport did Harold play from 1961 to 1971?

650. In 1979/80 Harold managed Bristol Rovers, who replaced him?

# NATHAN ELLINGTON

651. In which year was Nathan was born in Bradford –
1979, 1980 or 1981

652. How many League goals did Nathan score in his Rovers
career?

653. In which year did Nathan join the Pirates from Walton
& Hersham?

654. Following on from the previous question, how much
did Rovers pay for Nathan?

655. How many League appearances did Nathan make for
Rovers?

656. Against which team did Nathan make his Pirates debut
when he come on as a substitute at home?

657. Which club did Nathan join when he left the Pirates?

658. Following on from the previous question, in which year
did Nathan leave?

659. Against which team did Nathan score his first Rovers
goal in a 2-0 win, coming on as a substitute?

660. Against which Premier League team did Nathan score
a hat-trick in a 3-1 FA Cup win in January 2002?

# GARY MABBUTT

661. Gary was born on 23 August in which year – 1959, 1961 or 1963?

662. At which club did Gary start his professional football career?

663. True or false: Gary is the nephew of former Rovers stalwart Ray Mabbutt?

664. How many League appearances did Gary make for Rovers – 118, 120 or 122?

665. In Gary's career at the Pirates how many goals did he score in League and cup matches?

666. In 1982 Gary signed for Tottenham Hotspur, what was the transfer fee - £105,000, £110,000 or £115,000?

667. Gary went on to win two cups with Tottenham could you name them both?

668. Gary also played at international level for England, how many full England caps did he gain between 1982 and 1992?

669. True or false: Gary once appeared on the BBC's Blue Peter demonstrating how to inject insulin into an orange to show how he dealt with his diabetes?

670. Gary was awarded which honour in January 1994 for his services to football?

# RAY GRAYDON

671. What was Ray training to be when he started his football career with Rovers?

672. How many League goals did Ray score for Rovers in his career – 31, 33 or 35?

673. Against which team did Ray make his League debut during September 1965?

674. In which year did Ray leave Rovers?

675. Which Midlands team did Ray manage between 1998 and 2002?

676. Which club did Ray sign for when he left Bristol Rovers?

677. Following on from the previous question, which player came to Bristol Rovers as part of the deal and £25,000?

678. In which year was Ray appointed Bristol Rovers manager?

679. How many League appearances did Ray make for Rovers in his career?

680. In which year did Ray leave as Rovers manager – 2004, 2005 or 2006?

# BARRY HAYLES

681.   Barry was born on 17 May in which year – 1968, 1970 or 1972?

682.   At which non-League club did Barry start his career in 1995?

683.   In which position does Barry play?

684.   In May 1997 Barry signed for Rovers, what was the transfer fee?

685.   Barry made 62 League appearances for Rovers, how many League goals did he score?

686.   Barry scored a goal in each of his first three games for Rovers matching the achievements of which other two former Pirates?

687.   True or false: Barry finished his first season with Rovers as the 2nd Division's highest scorer with 23 goals?

688.   In 1999 Barry scored his last goal for Rovers; a stunning turn and volley from outside the box, who were Rovers opponents in this game?

689.   In 1999 which club did Barry sign for helping them through two promotions to get to the Premier league?

690.   In 2005 Barry played the last of his ten matches at international level for which Country?

# DERBIES: ROVERS V CITY

**691.** Can you name the Rovers player who scored in the 1-0 aggregate win over the two legs in the Football League Trophy, Southern Final second leg during February 2007?

**692.** True or false: Rovers won the first game between the two sides, played in September 1922 away from home?

**693.** Rovers played City in the League during 1991/1992, in which competition did they meet?

**694.** True or false: City beat Rovers during 1997/1998 in the League at home and away?

**695.** Who were the Rovers scorers in the 2-0 home win during April 2000 in the League?

**696.** Who finished higher in the League during 1999/2000 – Rovers or City?

**697.** Who scored a 90th minute equaliser against City in the 1-1 away draw during December 1996 in the League?

**698.** Which two players scored in the 4-2 home League defeat in March 1996?

**699.** What was the score when the sides met in Division Three during April 1988 at home?

**700.** How many times in the League did the sides meet during the 1970s?

# BRIAN GODFREY

701. Brian was born on 1 May in which year – 1940, 1942 or 1944?

702. Where was Brian born – Rhyl, Hollywell or Flint?

703. At which club did Brian start his professional career in 1960 where he only played one game?

704. In September 1971 Brian joined Bristol Rovers for £35,000 from which club did he sign?

705. An early highlight of Brian's Rovers career in the season of 1971/72 was a hat-trick against Bradford City what was the final score of this game?

706. Brian was a member of the team who won the 1972/73 pre season Watney Cup 7-6 on penalties who did they beat in the final?

707. How many League appearances did Brian make for The Gas – 79, 89 or 99?

708. In June 1973 Brian left Rovers in a transfer deal worth £10,000 which club did he join?

709. How many international appearances did Brian make for Wales?

710. With which non-League club did Brian have success as a player/manager winning the Southern League Championship in 1977/78 and taking them to the 1st Round of the FA Cup?

# BOBBY JONES

711.   What was Bobby known as, his nickname?

712.   How many League appearances did Bobby make for Rovers?

713.   Where on the pitch did Bobby play – left, centre or right?

714.   How many FA Cup goals did Bobby score for the Pirates – 5, 6 or 7?

715.   True or false: Bobby scored two goals on his debut at Middlesbrough?

716.   Following on from the previous question, in which year did he make his Rovers debut?

717.   In which year was Bobby born in Bristol – 1936, 1938 or 1940?

718.   Which two clubs did Bobby play for in between the two spells at Rovers?

719.   How many League goals did Bobby score for Rovers in his career – 101, 121 or 141?

720.   How much did Bobby cost the Pirates when he signed for his second spell, only being away for 11 months?

# ANDY TILLSON

721. Andy was born on 30 June in which year – 1964, 1966 or 1968?

722. Where was Andy born – Huntingdon, Northampton or Cambridge?

723. At which non-League club did Andy start his football career in 1987?

724. What position did Andy play at Rovers?

725. In 1993 from which club did Andy join Rovers for the club's record transfer fee of £370,000?

726. How many League appearances did Andy make for the Pirates – 250, 255 or 260?

727. How many League goals did Andy score while at The Gas?

728. How many years did Andy spend at Rovers?

729. Andy moved on a free transfer to which club in 2000, a club he captained to promotion to Division One?

730. Andy returned to the West Country as player/coach at Team Bath, which former Rovers goalkeeper did he work with at Team Bath?

# POT LUCK – 2

731.    Which team beat the Pirates 3-2 after extra time in the Football League Trophy Final in 2006/2007?

732.    Following on from the previous question, where was the game played?

733.    In which year were the club winners of the Southern League?

734.    What is the capacity of the Memorial Stadium - 9,916, 10,916 or 11,916?

735.    Which team knocked the Pirates out of the 2008 FA Cup having reached the quarter-finals?

736.    True of false: Between 1899 and 1919 the club wore black and white?

737.    In which film was Danny Butterman played by Nick Frost seen wearing a Bristol Rovers shirt?

738.    How many times have the club won the Gloucestershire Cup?

739.    The Bristol Rovers centre of excellence is associated with the Bristol Academy of Sport, at which college are they located?

740.    True or false: During 1999/2000 Bristol Rovers played in the Premier League?

# CARL SAUNDERS

**741.** Carl was born on 26 November in which year – 1964, 1966 or 1968?

**742.** Where was Carl born – Birmingham, Nottingham or Oldham?

**743.** In 1990 which club did Carl sign from to join Rovers?

**744.** What was the transfer fee from the above question – £50,000, £60,000 or £70,000?

**745.** In 1991/92 3rd Round of the FA Cup Rovers beat Plymouth Argyle 5-0, how many of the five goals did Carl score?

**746.** In the 4th Round of the 1991/92 FA Cup Carl scored a 25-yard volley against which goalkeeper?

**747.** How many League appearances did Carl make for Rovers – 123, 134, or 145?

**748.** How many League goals did Carl score for the Pirates in his three years at the club?

**749.** Which team did Carl join in 1993 after leaving Rovers?

**750.** After Carl retired from the game he joined the Avon and Somerset Police, what job did he do for them?

# LEAGUE GOALSCORERS – 2

*Match the number of league goals they scored
for the club against the player*

| | | |
|---|---|---|
| 751. | Dai Ward | 0 |
| 752. | Stuart Taylor | 2 |
| 753. | Gary Penrice | 4 |
| 754. | Vic Lambden | 11 |
| 755. | Geoff Fox | 13 |
| 756. | Andy Tillson | 28 |
| 757. | Joe Davis | 41 |
| 758. | Ian Holloway | 60 |
| 759. | Lindsay Parsons | 90 |
| 760. | Mark Walters | 117 |

# PRE-WORLD-WAR 1 & 2
# FA CUP WINS

*Match the season/round with the result*

761.  1901/02 1st Round

Rovers 2 – 0
Notts County

762.  1938/39 1st Round

Rovers 2 – 1
Southport

763.  1932/33 1st Round

Rovers 2 – 0
Chesterfield

764.  1926/27 1st Round

Rovers 1 – 0
Middlesbrough

765.  1907/08 2nd Round replay

Rovers 3 – 1
Queens Park
Rangers

766.  1912/13 1st Round

Dartford 0 – 1
Rovers

767.  1930/31 3rd Round

Rovers 1 – 0
Torquay United

768.  1934/35 2nd Round

Rovers 4 – 1
Cardiff City

769.  1936/37 2nd Round

Rovers 4 – 2
Walsall

770.  1927/28 1st Round

Rovers 4 – 1
Peterborough
United

# LEGENDS

*Rearrange the letters to make the name of a Rovers legend*

771.   VIDAD WMSLIALI

772.   KIECJA TITP

773.   TPEER NMASSPO

774.   HONJ TGALNIW

775.   USTRTA YTRLOA

776.   YRA TUMBTBA

777.   YAND NLTLOSI

778.   GROGEE DGEPBRIEERHT

779.   NUAVGAH SEJNO

780.   LYDAISN PSSNORA

# POST WORLD-WAR 2 FA CUP WINS

### Match the season/round with the result

| | | |
|---|---|---|
| 781. | 1977/78 3rd Round | Bath City 0 – 5 Rovers |
| 782. | 2007/08 5th Round | Rovers 3 – 0 Hull City |
| 783. | 1951/52 2nd Round | Rovers 2 – 0 Weymouth Town |
| 784. | 1967/68 2nd Round | Coventry City 1 – 2 Rovers |
| 785. | 1971/72 2nd Round | Rovers 1 – 0 Southampton |
| 786. | 1994/95 1st Round | Rovers 5 – 0 Mansfield Town |
| 787. | 1963/64 2nd Round | Sunderland 0 – 1 Rovers |
| 788. | 1985/86 3rd Round | Rovers 3 – 0 Cambridge United |
| 789. | 1950/51 5th Round | Wimbledon 0 – 4 Rovers |
| 790. | 1957/58 3rd Round | Rovers 3 – 1 Leicester City |

# LEAGUE GOALSCORERS – 3

*Match the number of league goals they scored for the club against the player*

| | | |
|---|---|---|
| 791. | Mike Barrett | 0 |
| 792. | Brian Godfrey | 11 |
| 793. | Ray Warren | 66 |
| 794. | Kenny Stephens | 3 |
| 795. | David Williams | 10 |
| 796. | Jason Roberts | 60 |
| 797. | Phil Bater | 38 |
| 798. | Gary Mabbutt | 16 |
| 799. | Steve Yates | 18 |
| 800. | Ian Hamilton | 28 |

# ANSWERS

## HISTORY OF THE CLUB
1.     *1883*
2.     *Black Arabs*
3.     *1898*
4.     *17 February 1899*
5.     *The Pirates and The Gas*
6.     *Bristol City*
7.     *Sheffield United*
8.     *Memorial Stadium*
9.     *Whaddon Road, Cheltenham Town's ground*
10.     *Fulham*

## WHO AM I? – 1
11.     *Steve Phillips*
12.     *Jack Pitt*
13.     *Joe Jacobson*
14.     *Vitalijs Astafjevs*
15.     *Gary Mabbutt*
16.     *Stuart Taylor*
17.     *Rickie Lambert*
18.     *Alan Ball*
19.     *Jo Kuffour*
20.     *Bobby Gould*

## MANAGERS - 1
| | | |
|---|---|---|
| 21. | *Gerry Francis* | *1987-1991* |
| 22. | *Bobby Gould* | *1981-83* |
| 23. | *Terry Cooper* | *1980-81* |
| 24. | *Bert Tann* | *1950-1968* |
| 25 | *Andy Wilson* | *1921-26* |
| 26. | *John Ward* | *1993-96* |
| 27. | *Ian Holloway* | *1996-2001* |
| 28. | *Don Megson* | *1972-77* |
| 29. | *Joe Palmer* | *1926-29* |
| 30. | *Albert Prince-Cox* | *1930-36* |

## STEVE WHITE

31.      Two
32.      Chipping Sodbury, Gloucestershire
33.      44
34.      Striker
35.      151: 135 (16)
36.      David Williams
37.      £35,000
38.      Joe White
39.      Swindon Town
40.      Chippenham Town

## HONOURS

| 41. | League Cup Quarter-Finals | 1971/72 |
|-----|---------------------------|---------|
| 42. | Division Three Cup Winners | 1934/35 |
| 43. | League Two Play-off Winners | 2006/07 |
| 44. | Division Two Play-off Runners-up | 1994/95 |
| 45. | Watney Cup Winners | 1971/72 |
| 46. | Champions Division Three | 1989/90 |
| 47. | FA Cup Quarter-Finals | 1957/58 |
| 48. | Southern League Champions | 1904/05 |
| 49. | Division Three Runners-up | 1973/74 |
| 50. | Champions Division Three (South) | 1952/53 |

## DAVID MEHEW

51.      1967
52.      Leeds United
53.      195 (27)
54.      10
55.      63
56.      Leyland Daf Cup
57.      Boris
58.      Walsall
59.      True
60.      Bobby Gould

## WHERE DID THEY GO? – 1

61.      Junior Agogo            Nottingham Forest

| 62. | Nathan Ellington | Wigan Athletic |
| 63. | Barry Hayles | Fulham |
| 64. | Jamie Cureton | Reading |
| 65. | Gary Penrice | Watford |
| 66. | Scott Sinclair | Chelsea |
| 67. | Tony Pounder | Weymouth |
| 68. | Gareth Taylor | Crystal Palace |
| 69. | Devon White | Cambridge United |
| 70. | Marcus Stewart | Huddersfield Town |

## 2008/2009

71. Carlisle United
72. Darryl Duffy and Rickie Lambert
73. Southend United
74. Rickie Lambert
75. Jo Kuffour
76. Paul Trollope
77. Ben Hunt
78. Leicester City
79. Colchester United
80. Rickie Lambert

## KENNY HIBBITT

81. 1951
82. Bradford
83. 16
84. Two
85. 1986
86. Coventry City
87. 53
88. True
89. False: Gerry Francis
90. True

## 2007/2008

91. Port Vale
92. Paul Trollope
93. Carlisle United

94.   Chris Lines, Craig Hamilton and Andrew Williams
95.   True: 1 win and 2 draws
96.   Rickie Lambert
97.   Rickie Lambert
98.   Craig Disley
99.   Daniel Coles
100.  True

## NATIONALITIES – 1

| 101. | Glyn Jones | Welsh |
| 102. | Guy Ipoua | Cameroonian |
| 103. | Mickey Evans | Irish |
| 104. | Vitalijs Astafjevs | Latvian |
| 105. | Aidan McCaffrey | English |
| 106. | Gino Padula | Argentinean |
| 107. | Scott Howie | Scottish |
| 108. | Nigel Pierre | Trinidad & Tobagonian |
| 109. | Moussa Dagnogo | French |
| 110. | Giuliano Grazioli | Italian |

## WHO AM I? - 2

111.  Lennie Lawrence
112.  Esmond Million
113.  Paul Trollope
114.  Darryl Duffy
115.  Nick Culkin
116.  Jamie Cureton
117.  Craig Hinton
118.  Andy Thomson
119.  Byron Anthony
120.  Gary Penrice

## WHERE DID THEY COME FROM – 1

| 121. | Craig Disley | Mansfield Town |
| 122. | Gerry Francis | Portsmouth |
| 123. | Bobby Gould | Wolverhampton Wanderers |
| 124. | Ian Holloway | Queens Park Rangers |
| 125. | Kenny Hibbitt | Coventry City |

| 126. | Geoff Twentyman | Preston North End |
| 127. | Carl Saunders | Stoke City |
| 128. | John Scales | Leeds United |
| 129. | David Pipe | Notts County |
| 130. | Che Wilson | Norwich City |

## LEAGUE DEBUTS

| 131. | David Pipe | 1-1 draw against Port Vale (away), August 2007 |
| 132. | Ben Hunt | 1-1 draw against Brighton & Hove Albion (away), August 2008 |
| 133. | Stuart Campbell | 2-0 defeat against Mansfield (away), August 2004 |
| 134. | Andrew Williams | 1-1 draw against Port Vale (away), August 2007 |
| 135. | Steve Elliott | 2-0 defeat against Mansfield (away), August 2004 |
| 136. | Charlie Clough | 2-0 defeat against Brighton & Hove Albion (home), April 2008 |
| 137. | Matt Groves | 2-1 defeat against Huddersfield Town (away), December 2007 |
| 138. | Craig Disley | 4-2 defeat against Leyton Orient (away), September 2004 |
| 139. | Charles Reece | 3-0 win against Carlisle United (home), December 2007 |
| 140. | Steve Phillips | 4-1 defeat against Peterborough United (away), August 2006 |

## ROVERS WINS IN LEAGUE DERBIES

| 141. | Division Three (South) 5 May 1936 | Rovers 3 – 1 City |
| 142. | Division Three (South) 23 September 1922 | City 0 – 1 Rovers |
| 143. | League Two 22 April 2000 | Rovers 2 – 0 City |
| 144. | Division One 13 December 1992 | Rovers 4 – 0 City |
| 145. | Division Three 12 April 1982 | City 1 – 2 Rovers |
| 146. | Division Three (South) 30 December 1950 | Rovers 2 –1 City |
| 147. | Division Three (South) 30 December 1933 | Rovers 5 – 1 City |
| 148. | Division Three (South) 7 September 1935 | City 0 – 2 Rovers |
| 149. | Division Three 2 May 1990 | Rovers 3 – 0 City |

150.     Division Three 12 April 1988          Rovers 1 – 0 City

## MATCH THE YEAR – 1
151.     Finished runners-up of the Football League Trophy   2007
152.     Club moved to Twerton Park                          1986
153.     Paul Trollope takes over as Pirates manager         2005
154.     Club formed Bristol Rovers ladies team              1998
155.     Fulham pay £2.1 million for Barry Hayles            1998
156.     Bristol Rovers beat Shrewsbury Town 7-0
         in Division Three                                   1964
157.     Ian Halloway takes over as Rovers manager           1996
158.     Bristol Rovers beat Swansea City 7-0
          in Division Two                                    1954
159.     Rovers beat Brighton & Hove Albion 7-0
         in Division Three South                             1952
160.     Gerry Francis left Rovers as manager                1991

## IAN HOLLOWAY
161.     1963
162.     Bristol
163.     Bristol Rovers
164.     False: Four times, three as a player and one as manager
165.     379
166.     True
167.     Queens Park Rangers
168.     Plymouth Argyle
169.     Bristol City
170.     True

## 2006/2007
171.     Sixth
172.     Grimsby Town
173.     Paul Trollope
174.     Richard Walker
175.     £200,000
176.     Stuart Campbell
177.     Richard Walker
178.     Rickie Lambert

179.   20
180.   Hartlepool United

**GERRY FRANCIS**
181.   1951
182.   Chiswick
183.   Queens Park Rangers
184.   12
185.   Eight
186.   Don Revie
187.   Portsmouth
188.   True
189.   Tranmere Rovers
190.   2001

**PLAY-OFF FINAL WINNERS – 2007**
191.   Wembley
192.   3-1 to Bristol Rovers
193.   Shrewsbury Town
194.   Richard Walker (2) and Sammy Igoe
195.   Lincoln City
196.   7-4: 2-1 and 5-3
197.   Richard Walker
198.   61,589
199.   Steve Phillips, Ryan Green, Bryon Anthony, Steve Elliott, Chris
       Carruthers, Lewis Haldene, Craig Disley, Stuart Campbell,
       Sammy Igoe, Rickie Lambert and Richard Walker
200.   Sean Rigg

**BOBBY GOULD**
201.   1946
202.   Coventry
203.   £10,000
204.   12
205.   Geoff Hurst
206.   Liverpool
207.   Wales
208.   Italy

209.  *False: Hawke's Bay United is in New Zealand*
210.  *True*

## MARCUS BROWNING
211.  *1971*
212.  *Midfielder*
213.  *Peter Beadle*
214.  *13*
215.  *Two*
216.  *Bournemouth*
217.  *152 (22)*
218.  *Huddersfield Town*
219.  *Wales*
220.  *Five*

## TONY PULIS
221.  *1958*
222.  *Welsh*
223.  *Bristol Rovers*
224.  *19*
225.  *True*
226.  *Eight*
227.  *130*
228.  *Gillingham*
229.  *False: It was April 2007*
230.  *Stoke City*

## HARRY BAMFORD
231.  *Right back*
232.  *Third Division South Championship 1952/1953*
233.  *1958*
234.  *Arsenal*
235.  *1920*
236.  *486*
237.  *Zero*
238.  *Brough Fletcher*
239.  *Five*
240.  *Bert Tann*

## WHERE DID THEY GO? – 2

| | | |
|---|---|---|
| 241. | Lee Thorpe | Swansea City |
| 242. | Adam Barrett | Southend United |
| 243. | Marcus Browning | Huddersfield Town |
| 244. | Gary Mabbutt | Tottenham Hotspur |
| 245. | Nigel Martyn | Crystal palace |
| 246. | Mick Channon | Norwich City |
| 247. | Paul Hendrie | Halifax Town |
| 248. | Brian Parkin | Wycombe Wanderers |
| 249. | Darren Mullings | Torquay United |
| 250. | Steve Foster | Doncaster Rovers |

## 1990s

| | |
|---|---|
| 251. | Robbie Pethick and David Hillier |
| 252. | 13th |
| 253. | John Ward |
| 254. | Marcus Stewart |
| 255. | Fourth |
| 256. | Malcolm Allison |
| 257. | Millwall |
| 258. | 13th |
| 259. | Ian Wright |
| 260. | Andy Reece |

## WHERE DID THEY COME FROM? – 2

| | | |
|---|---|---|
| 261. | Richard Walker | Blackpool |
| 262. | Tony Sealy | Swindon Town |
| 263. | Julian Alsop | Halesowen Town |
| 264. | Aaron Lescott | Stockport County |
| 265. | Paul Hardyman | Sunderland |
| 266. | Danny Coles | Hull City |
| 267. | Terry Cooper | Bristol City |
| 268. | Scott Howie | Reading |
| 269. | Aidan McCaffrey | Derby County |
| 270. | Matthew Lockwood | Queens Park Rangers |

## 2005/2006

| | |
|---|---|
| 271. | Ian Atkins |

272. Paul Trollope
273. 12th
274. Scott Shearer
275. Leyton Orient
276. Richard Walker
277. Junior Agogo
278. Craig Disley and Junior Agogo
279. 17
280. Richard Walker

## JAMIE CURETON

281. 1975
282. Bristol
283. Norwich City
284. 165
285. 72
286. Reading
287. South Korea
288. Derby County and Southend United
289. True
290. Robert Earnshaw

## 2004/2005

291. Ian Atkins
292. False: one win and four draws
293. Mansfield Town
294. Aaron Lescott
295. Junior Agogo
296. 21
297. 12th
298. Richard Walker
299. Richard Walker
300. Mansfield Town

## POSITIONS IN LEAGUE TWO

301. 1996/97       17th
302. 2005/06       12th
303. 1993/94       8th

| 304. | 1999/2000 | 7th |
| 305. | 2006/07 | 6th |
| 306. | 2000/01 | 21st |
| 307. | 1994/95 | 4th |
| 308. | 1998/99 | 13th |
| 309. | 1995/96 | 10th |
| 310. | 1997/98 | 5th |

## PETER AITKEN

| 311. | Cardiff |
| 312. | Central defender |
| 313. | Don Megson, Bobby Campbell and Harold Jarman |
| 314. | Three |
| 315. | Welsh |
| 316. | One |
| 317. | York City |
| 318. | 230 (4) |
| 319. | Bristol City |
| 320. | Football in the Community Officer |

## POSITIONS IN LEAGUE THREE AND ENGLISH THIRD DIVISION

| 321. | 1969/70 | 3rd |
| 322. | 2002/03 | 20th |
| 323. | 1989/90 | 1st |
| 324. | 1962/63 | 19th |
| 325. | 1982/83 | 7th |
| 326. | 2001/02 | 23rd |
| 327. | 1985/86 | 16th |
| 328. | 1966/67 | 5th |
| 329. | 2003/04 | 15th |
| 330. | 1973/74 | 2nd |

## MATCH THE YEAR – 2

| 331. | Malcolm Allison leaves Rovers as manager | 1993 |
| 332. | The club were formed as Black Arabs FC | 1883 |
| 333. | Finished runners-up of the Football League Trophy | 1990 |
| 334. | The Club reached the FA Cup quarter finals for the first time since 1958 | 2008 |

| 335. | Team worn pink shirts in a friendly against Plymouth Argyle | 2006 |
|---|---|---|
| 336. | The Club moved to Eastville Stadium | 1897 |
| 337. | Bobby Gould takes over as manager (2nd spell) | 1985 |
| 338. | The Club won the Third Division title | 1990 |
| 339. | Ron Gingell took over as manager, managing them for one game | 1981 |
| 340. | The club moved to the Memorial Ground | 1996 |

## NATIONALITIES – 2

| 341. | Joe Jacobson | Welsh |
|---|---|---|
| 342. | Ciaran Toner | Irish |
| 343. | Marcus Andreasson | Swedish |
| 344. | Michele Di Piedi | Italian |
| 345. | Stephane Leoni | French |
| 346. | Alistair Gibb | English |
| 347. | Sam Oji | Nigerian |
| 348. | Sandy McCubbin | Scottish |
| 349. | Barry Hayles | Jamaican |
| 350. | Junior Agogo | Ghanaian |

## 2003/2004

351. Darlington

352. 15th

353. Paul Tait

354. 14

355. Lee Hodges

356. Five

357. Ray Graydon, Phil Bater, Russell Osman, Kevan Broadhurst and Ian Atkins

358. Ali Gibb

359. Danny Williams, Adam Barrett and Ali Gibb

360. Paul Tait

## NIGEL MARTYN

361. 1966

362. St. Austell

363. Midfield

364. St. Blazey
365. 101
366. True
367. Crystal Palace
368. Crystal Palace & Leeds United
369. Russia
370. 23

## IAN ALEXANDER

371. Glasgow
372. Bobby Gould
373. Six
374. Ian 'Jocky' Alexander
375. 284 (7)
376. True
377. Bristol City
378. 1986
379. Brighton & Hove Albion
380. Yate Town

## GARY PENRICE

381. 1964
382. Bristol
383. Bristol City
384. Mangotsfield United
385. A qualified plumber
386. 1984
387. 234
388. 60
389. Watford
390. False: Head of Recruitment for Leicester City

## 2002/2003

391. Swansea
392. Giuliano Grazioli
393. 20th
394. Ray Graydon
395. Giuliano Grazioli

396. *Shrewsbury Town*
397. *Giuliano Grazioli*
398. *Birmingham City*
399. *Andy Rammell*
400. *Andy Rammell*

## SQUAD NUMBERS – 1 2008-2009

| | | |
|---|---|---|
| 401. | *Rickie Lambert* | *9* |
| 402. | *Craig Disley* | *20* |
| 403. | *Steve Phillips* | *1* |
| 404. | *Aaron Lescott* | *32* |
| 405. | *Steve Elliott* | *6* |
| 406. | *Danny Coles* | *16* |
| 407. | *Darryl Duffy* | *10* |
| 408. | *Ryan Green* | *2* |
| 409. | *Steve Book* | *33* |
| 410. | *Chris Lines* | *4* |

## *1980s*

411. *Billy Clark*
412. *Eighth*
413. *Gerry Francis*
414. *Fifth*
415. *Two: 1981-1985 and 1987-1991 (and again between 1996-2000)*
416. *Three*
417. *1984*
418. *15th*
419. *Torquay United*
420. *John Scales*

## BRISTOL CUP/TROPHY DERBIES

| | | |
|---|---|---|
| 421. | *FA Cup 10 December 1983* | *Rovers 1 – 2 City* |
| 422. | *FA Cup 15 February 1958* | *City 3 – 4 Rovers* |
| 423. | *FA Cup 27 January 1968* | *City 0 – 0 Rovers* |
| 424. | *FA Cup 8 December 19* | *City 4 – 2 Rovers* |
| 425. | *League Cup 8 October 1991* | *City 2 – 4 Rovers* |
| 426. | *FA Cup 8 December 1984* | *City 1 –3 Rovers* |

| 427. | FA Cup 10 January 1925 | Rovers 0 – 1 City |
| 428. | Johnstone's Paint Trophy 27 February 2007 | Rovers 1 – 0 City |
| 429. | LDV Vans Trophy 9 January 20 | City 3 – 0 Rovers |
| 430. | League Cup 12 August 1997 | City 0 – 0 Rovers |

## GERAINT WILLIAMS

431. 1962
432. Eight
433. Cardiff City
434. David
435. Ipswich Town and Colchester United
436. Sheffield Wednesday
437. 13
438. Midfielder
439. 138 (3)
440. Derby County

## CLUB RECORDS

441. 7-0
442. 15-1
443. 6-0
444. Luton Town
445. Geoff Bradford
446. 546
447. 242
448. Queens Park Rangers
449. Fulham & West Bromwich Albion
450. 92

## 1970s

451. 1971
452. 16th
453. 1971 and 1972
454. Don Megson
455. Second
456. Division Two
457. 1974 and 1975
458. 18th

459. **Brighton & Hove Albion**

460. **Alan Warboys and Bruce Bannister**

## SQUAD NUMBERS 2008-2009 – 2

| | | |
|---|---|---|
| 461. | Tom Parrinello | 21 |
| 462. | Joe Jacobson | 3 |
| 463. | Alex Kite | 24 |
| 464. | Andrew Williams | 8 |
| 465. | Craig Hinton | 5 |
| 466. | Jeff Hughes | 11 |
| 467. | David Pipe | 14 |
| 468. | Ryan Paddock | 23 |
| 469. | Stuart Campbell | 7 |
| 470. | Mike Green | 13 |

## 2001/2002

471. **Steve Foster**

472. **Gerry Francis**

473. **True: one draw and four defeats**

474. **23rd**

475. **Nathan Ellington**

476. **Nathan Ellington**

477. **Sergio Ommel**

478. **Leyton Orient**

479. **Nathan Ellington**

480. **Wayne Carlisle**

## STUART TAYLOR

481. **1947**

482. **Central Defender**

483. **True**

484. **For the most career Bristol Rovers appearances**

485. **Bert Tann**

486. **28**

487. **False: he has never managed Rovers in his career**

488. **546**

489. **1980**

490. **Don Megson**

## JIM EADIE
491. *1947*
492. *183*
493. *Goalkeeper*
494. *The flying pig (from Kirkintilloch)*
495. *Promotion from the Third Division*
496. *Cardiff City*
497. *True*
498. *Scottish*
499. *Bath City*
500. *1977*


## BRUCE BANNISTER
501. *1947*
502. *Bradford*
503. *Bradford City*
504. *'Smash and Grab' Alan Warboys (Smash) and Bruce Bannister (Grab)*
505. *202*
506. *80*
507. *Plymouth Argyle*
508. *No*
509. *True*
510. *US Dunkerque*


## UNUSUAL RESULTS
511. *v. Lincoln City (away), Play-off semi-final, May 2007*      *5-3*
512. *v. Colchester United (away), League, January 2000*      *4-5*
513. *v. Walsall (home), League, October 1998*      *3-4*
514. *v. Mansfield Town (home), League, March 2005*      *4-4*
515. *v. Doncaster Rovers (away), League, October 2003*      *1-5*
516. *v. Shrewsbury Town (away), League, September 2002*      *5-2*
517. *v. Mansfield Town (away), League, December 2005*      *3-3*
518. *v. Oxford United (home), League, April 2001*      *6-2*
519. *v. Macclesfield Town (away), League, May 1999*      *4-3*
520. *v. Luton Town (home), League, September 2000*      *3-3*

## PETER BEADLE

521.  1972
522.  Lambeth
523.  Watford
524.  Bury
525.  98
526.  Port Vale
527.  True
528.  Ten minutes
529.  Clevedon Town
530.  False: He was sacked as manager of Newport County

## 2000/2001

531.  Cambridge
532.  Ian Holloway
533.  Gary Penrice and Garry Thompson
534.  Micky Evans
535.  Nathan Ellington
536.  £10,000
537.  Colchester United
538.  21st
539.  Lewis Hogg
540.  Wrexham

## ALFIE BIGGS

541.  1936
542.  Bristol
543.  Preston North End
544.  37
545.  424
546.  178
547.  Manchester United
548.  Geoff Bradford and Ian Hamilton
549.  Walsall
550.  True

## BIG WINS

551.  v. Chester City (home), League, December 2004          4-1

| 552. | v. Hereford United (home), League, August 2008 | 6-1 |
| 553. | v. Rushden & Diamonds (home), FA Cup 2nd round, December 2007 | 5-1 |
| 554. | v. Accrington Stanley (home), League, December 2006 | 4-0 |
| 555. | v. Bournemouth (home), League, December 1997 | 5-3 |
| 556. | v. Bath City (away), FA Cup 1st round, November 1994 | 5-0 |
| 557. | v. Barnet (home), League, March 1994 | 5-2 |
| 558. | v. Brentford (away), League, September 2000 | 6-2 |
| 559. | v. Bristol City (home), League, December 1992 | 4-0 |
| 560. | v. Exeter City (home), FA Cup 2nd round, December 1998 | 5-0 |

## GEOFF BRADFORD

561. 1927
562. Soundwell
563. Crystal Palace
564. 'Rip' after Rip Van Winkle
565. True
566. 461
567. 242
568. Geoff made his one and only appearance for England
569. Denmark
570. False: Geoff is the only player to represent England from Bristol Rovers

## 1960s

571. Bert Tann, Fred Ford and Bill Dodgin (Snr)
572. 16th
573. 1962
574. Division Three
575. Sixth
576. Blue pinstripes
577. 4-4
578. 19th
579. Gloucestershire Cup
580. Bristol City

## TOP GOALSCORERS

581. Harold Jarman     143

| 582. | Bruce Bannister | 93 |
| 583. | Alfie Biggs | 197 |
| 584. | Geoff Bradford | 260 |
| 585. | Peter Hooper | 107 |
| 586. | Bobby Jones | 110 |
| 587. | Vic Lambden | 133 |
| 588. | George Petherbridge | 92 |
| 589. | Paul Randall | 106 |
| 590. | Dai Ward | 96 |

## POT LUCK – 1

| 591. | 1972 |
| 592. | Sunderland |
| 593. | 53 |
| 594. | 2007 |
| 595. | 151 |
| 596. | 1934/1935 |
| 597. | Because they used to play at the Eastville Stadium which was located next to a gas works |
| 598. | Goodnight, Irene |
| 599. | BS7 0AQ |
| 600. | £370,000 |

## YEARS AT THE CLUB

| 601. | Phil Bater | 1974-1981 |
| 602. | Brian Parkin | 1989-1996 |
| 603. | Harold Jarman | 1959-1973 |
| 604. | Kenny Stephens | 1970-1978 |
| 605. | Andy Tillson | 1992-2000 |
| 606. | Jason Roberts | 1998-2000 |
| 607. | Devon White | 1987-1992 |
| 608. | Steve White | 1977-1980 |
| 609. | Stuart Taylor | 1965-1980 |
| 610. | Vic Lambden | 1945-1955 |

## LEAGUE GOALSCORERS – 1

| 611. | Larry Lloyd | 1 |
| 612. | Bruce Bannister | 80 |

| 613. | Wayne Jones | 28 |
| 614. | Harold Jarman | 127 |
| 615. | Geoff Bradford | 242 |
| 616. | Ray Mabbutt | 27 |
| 617. | Vitalijs Astafjevs | 16 |
| 618. | Peter Hooper | 101 |
| 619. | Barry Hayles | 32 |
| 620. | Vaughan Jones | 12 |

## TOP APPEARANCES

| 621. | Harold Bamford | 524 |
| 622. | Ian Holloway | 453(18) |
| 623. | George Petherbridge | 496 |
| 624. | Ray Warren | 486 |
| 625. | Vaughan Jones | 437(14) |
| 626. | Alfie Biggs | 463 |
| 627. | Stuart Taylor | 627 |
| 628. | Geoff Bradford | 511 |
| 629. | Harold Jarman | 502(13) |
| 630. | Bobby Jones | 461(12) |

## 1950s

| 631. | Bert Tann |
| 632. | 10th |
| 633. | Geoff Bradford |
| 634. | Manchester United |
| 635. | Sixth |
| 636. | Division Two |
| 637. | 1952/1953 |
| 638. | One |
| 639. | 9th |
| 640. | 1951 and 1958 |

## HAROLD JARMAN

| 641. | 1939 |
| 642. | Bristol |
| 643. | 1959 |
| 644. | 440 |

645. *127*

646. *Newport County*

647. *New York Cosmos*

648. *Pele*

649. *Cricket*

650. *Terry Cooper*

## NATHAN ELLINGTON

651. *1981*

652. *35*

653. *1999*

654. *£150,000*

655. *76 (40)*

656. *Gillingham*

657. *Wigan Athletic*

658. *2002*

659. *York City*

660. *Derby County*

## GARY MABBUTT

661. *1961*

662. *Bristol Rovers*

663. *False: Gary is the son of Ray Mabbutt*

664. *122*

665. *12 – 10 League goals, one FA Cup goal and one League Cup goal*

666. *£105,000*

667. *Gary won the UEFA Cup in1984 and The FA Cup in 1991*

668. *16*

669. *True*

670. *Gary was awarded the MBE*

## RAY GRAYDON

671. *Electrician*

672. *33*

673. *Swansea*

674. *1971*

675. *Walsall*

676. *Aston Villa*

677.　Brian Godfrey
678.　2002
679.　131 (2)
680.　2004

## BARRY HAYLES

681.　1972
682.　Stevenage Borough
683.　Striker
684.　£200,000
685.　32
686.　Vic Lambden and Dennis Bailey
687.　True
688.　Walsall
689.　Fulham
690.　Jamaica

## DERBIES: ROVERS V CITY

691.　Rickie Lambert
692.　True
693.　League Cup
694.　True: 2-0 away and 2-1 at home
695.　Jason Roberts and Mark Walters
696.　Rovers: 7th and Bristol City 9th
697.　Peter Beadle
698.　Billy Clark and Andy Gurney
699.　1-0 to Rovers
700.　Four: twice during 1975/1976 and twice during 1974/1975

## BRIAN GODFREY

701.　1940
702.　Flint
703.　Everton
704.　Aston Villa
705.　Bristol Rovers 7 – 1 Bradford City
706.　Sheffield United
707.　79
708.　Newport County

709. **Three caps 1964-65**
710. **Bath City**

## BOBBY JONES

711. **The Eastville Flier**
712. **410 (11)**
713. **Left**
714. **Five**
715. **True**
716. **1957**
717. **1938**
718. **Northampton Town and Swindon Town**
719. **101**
720. **£8,000**

## ANDY TILLSON

721. **1966**
722. **Huntingdon**
723. **Kettering Town**
724. **Central Defender**
725. **Queens Park Rangers**
726. **250**
727. **Eleven**
728. **Eight**
729. **Walsall**
730. **Brian Parkin**

## POT LICK – 2

731. **Doncaster Rovers**
732. **Millennium Stadium**
733. **1905**
734. **11,916**
735. **West Bromwich Albion**
736. **True**
737. **Hot Fuzz**
738. **32**
739. **Filton College**
740. **False: the club have never played in the Premier League**

## CARL SAUNDERS

| | |
|---|---|
| 741. | 1964 |
| 742. | Birmingham |
| 743. | Stoke City |
| 744. | £70,000 |
| 745. | Four |
| 746. | Bruce Grobbelaar |
| 747. | 123 |
| 748. | 42 |
| 749. | Oxford United |
| 750. | Community Liaison Officer dealing with issues of race awareness |

## LEAGUE GOALSCORERS – 2

| | | |
|---|---|---|
| 751. | Dai Ward | 90 |
| 752. | Stuart Taylor | 28 |
| 753. | Gary Penrice | 60 |
| 754. | Vic Lambden | 117 |
| 755. | Geoff Fox | 2 |
| 756. | Andy Tillson | 11 |
| 757. | Joe Davis | 4 |
| 758. | Ian Holloway | 41 |
| 759. | Lindsay Parsons | 0 |
| 760. | Mark Walters | 13 |

## PRE WORLD-WAR 1 AND 2 FA CUP WINS

| | | |
|---|---|---|
| 761. | 1901/02 1st Round | Rovers 1 – 0 Middlesbrough |
| 762. | 1938/39 1st Round | Rovers 4 – 1 Peterborough United |
| 763. | 1932/33 1st Round | Rovers 4 – 1 Cardiff City |
| 764. | 1926/27 1st Round | Rovers 1 – 0 Torquay United |
| 765. | 1907/08 2nd Round replay | Rovers 2 – 0 Chesterfield |
| 766. | 1912/13 1st Round | Rovers 2 – 0 Notts County |
| 767. | 1930/31 3rd Round | Rovers 3 – 1 Queens Park Rangers |
| 768. | 1934/35 2nd Round | Dartford 0 – 1 Rovers |
| 769. | 1936/37 2nd Round | Rovers 2 – 1 Southport |
| 770. | 1927/28 1st Round | Rovers 4 – 2 Walsall |

## LEGENDS

771. David Williams
772. Jackie Pitt
773. Peter Sampson
774. John Watling
775. Stuart Taylor
776. Ray Mabbutt
777. Andy Tillson
778. George Petherbridge
779. Vaughan Jones
780. Lindsay Parsons

## POST WORLD-WAR 2 FA CUP WINS

| 781. | 1977/78 3rd Round | Sunderland 0 – 1 Rovers |
|------|-------------------|--------------------------|
| 782. | 2007/08 5th Round | Rovers 1 – 0 Southampton |
| 783. | 1951/52 2nd Round | Rovers 2 – 0 Weymouth Town |
| 784. | 1967/68 2nd Round | Wimbledon 0 – 4 Rovers |
| 785. | 1971/72 2nd Round | Rovers 3 – 0 Cambridge United |
| 786. | 1994/95 1st Round | Bath City 0 – 5 Rovers |
| 787. | 1963/64 2nd Round | Coventry City 1 – 2 Rovers |
| 788. | 1985/86 3rd Round | Rovers 3 – 1 Leicester City |
| 789. | 1950/51 5th Round | Rovers 3 – 0 Hull City |
| 790. | 1957/58 3rd Round | Rovers 5 – 0 Mansfield Town |

## LEAGUE GOALSCORERS – 3

| 791. | Mike Barrett | 18 |
|------|--------------|----|
| 792. | Brian Godfrey | 16 |
| 793. | Ray Warren | 28 |
| 794. | Kenny Stephens | 11 |
| 795. | David Williams | 66 |
| 796. | Jason Roberts | 38 |
| 797. | Phil Bater | 3 |
| 798. | Gary Mabbutt | 10 |
| 799. | Steve Yates | 0 |
| 800. | Ian Hamilton | 60 |

# NOTES

# NOTES

# NOTES

# NOTES

# NOTES

# NOTES

# NOTES

# NOTES

# NOTES

www.apexpublishing.co.uk